# play guitar with...

# the kooks

C000110923

**Wise Publications**
part of The Music Sales Group
London / New York / Paris / Sydney / Copenhagen / Berlin / Madrid / Tokyo

*Published by*
**Wise Publications**
*14-15 Berners Street, London W1T 3LJ, UK*

*Exclusive Distributors:*
**Music Sales Limited**
*Distribution Centre, Newmarket Road,*
*Bury St Edmunds, Suffolk IP33 3YB, UK*

**Music Sales Pty Limited**
*20 Resolution Drive,*
*Caringbah, NSW 2229, Australia*

Order No. AM989967
ISBN 978-1-84772-018-4
This book © Copyright 2008 Wise Publications,
a division of Music Sales Limited.

*Printed in the EU*


www.musicsales.com

*Compiled by Nick Crispin*
*Music arranged by Arthur Dick*
*Edited by Tom Farncombe*
*Music processed by Paul Ewers Music Design*

*All Guitars by Arthur Dick*
*Bass by Paul Townsend*
*Drums by Brett Morgan*
*Additional keyboards: Jonas Persson*

*CD recorded, mixed and mastered by Jonas Persson*

## Your Guarantee of Quality
*As publishers, we strive to produce every book*
*to the highest commercial standards.*
*The music has been freshly engraved and the book has*
*been carefully designed to minimise awkward page turns*
*and to make playing from it a real pleasure.*
*Particular care has been given to specifying acid-free,*
*neutral-sized paper made from pulps which have not been*
*elemental chlorine bleached. This pulp is from farmed*
*sustainable forests and was produced with special regard*
*for the environment.*
*Throughout, the printing and binding have been planned*
*to ensure a sturdy, attractive publication which should*
*give years of enjoyment.*
*If your copy fails to meet our high standards,*
*please inform us and we will gladly replace it.*

# guitar tablature explained

### Guitar music can be notated in three different ways: on a musical stave, in tablature, and in rhythm slashes.

RHYTHM SLASHES: are written above the stave. Strum chords in the rhythm indicated. Round noteheads indicate single notes.

THE MUSICAL STAVE: shows pitches and rhythms and is divided by lines into bars. Pitches are named after the first seven letters of the alphabet.

TABLATURE: graphically represents the guitar fingerboard. Each horizontal line represents a string, and each number represents a fret.

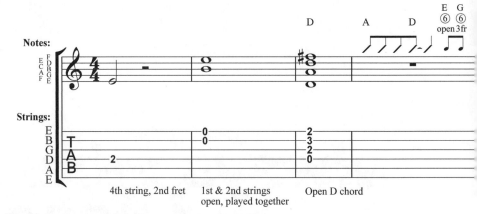

4th string, 2nd fret    1st & 2nd strings open, played together    Open D chord

## definitions for special guitar notation

SEMI-TONE BEND: Strike the note and bend up a semi-tone (½ step).

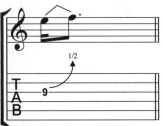

WHOLE-TONE BEND: Strike the note and bend up a whole-tone (full step).

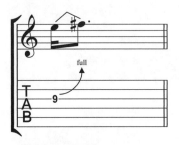

GRACE NOTE BEND: Strike the note and bend as indicated. Play the first note as quickly as possible.

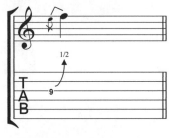

QUARTER-TONE BEND: Strike the note and bend up a ¼ step

BEND & RELEASE: Strike the note and bend up as indicated, then release back to the original note.

COMPOUND BEND & RELEASE: Strike the note and bend up and down in the rhythm indicated.

PRE-BEND: Bend the note as indicated, then strike it.

PRE-BEND & RELEASE: Bend the note as indicated. Strike it and release the note back to the original pitch.

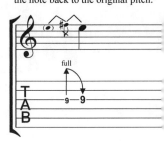

HAMMER-ON: Strike the first note with one finger, then sound the second note (on the same string) with another finger by fretting it without picking.

PULL-OFF: Place both fingers on the note to be sounded, strike the first note and without picking, pull the finger off to sound the second note.

LEGATO SLIDE (GLISS): Strike the first note and then slide the same fret-hand finger up or down to the second note. The second note is not struck.

MUFFLED STRINGS: A percussive sound is produced by laying the first hand across the string(s) without depressing, and striking them with the pick hand.

NATURAL HARMONIC: Strike the note while the fret-hand lightly touches the string directly over the fret indicated.

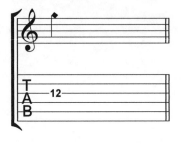

PICK SCRAPE: The edge of the pick is rubbed down (or up) the string, producing a scratchy sound.

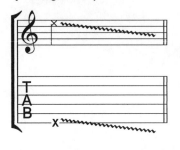

PALM MUTING: The note is partially muted by the pick hand lightly touching the string(s) just before the bridge.

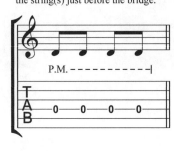

SHIFT SLIDE (GLISS & RESTRIKE Same as legato slide, except the second note is struck.

# always where i need to be

### Words & Music by Luke Pritchard

**Full performance demo: CD track 1**
**Backing only: CD track 9**

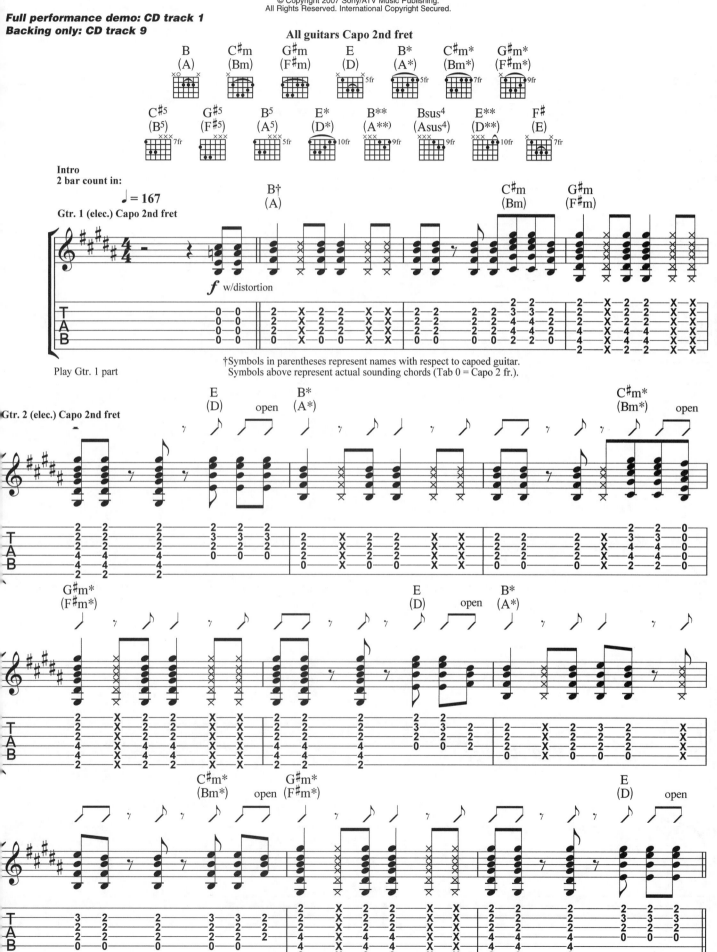

†Symbols in parentheses represent names with respect to capoed guitar.
Symbols above represent actual sounding chords (Tab 0 = Capo 2 fr.).

Play Gtr. 1 part

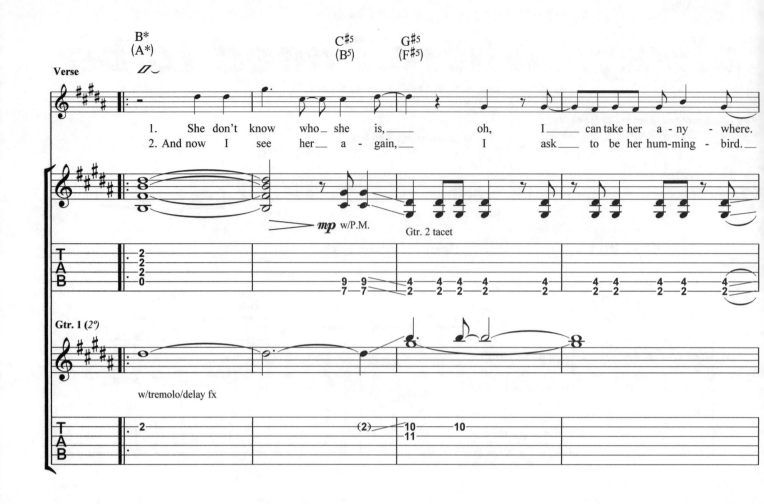

**Verse**

B* (A*)  C#5 (B5)  G#5 (F#5)

1. She don't know who she is,___ oh, I___ can take her a - ny - where.
2. And now I see her a - gain,___ I ask___ to be her hum-ming - bird.___

*mp* w/P.M.    Gtr. 2 tacet

**Gtr. 1 (2⁹)**

w/tremolo/delay fx

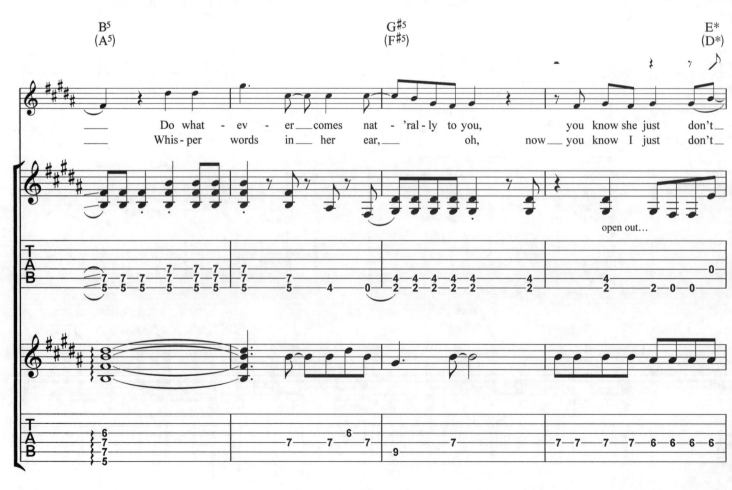

B5 (A5)  G#5 (F#5)  E* (D*)

___ Do what - ev - er___ comes nat-'ral - ly to you, you know she just don't___
___ Whis - per words in ___ her ear,___ oh, now___ you know I just don't___

open out...

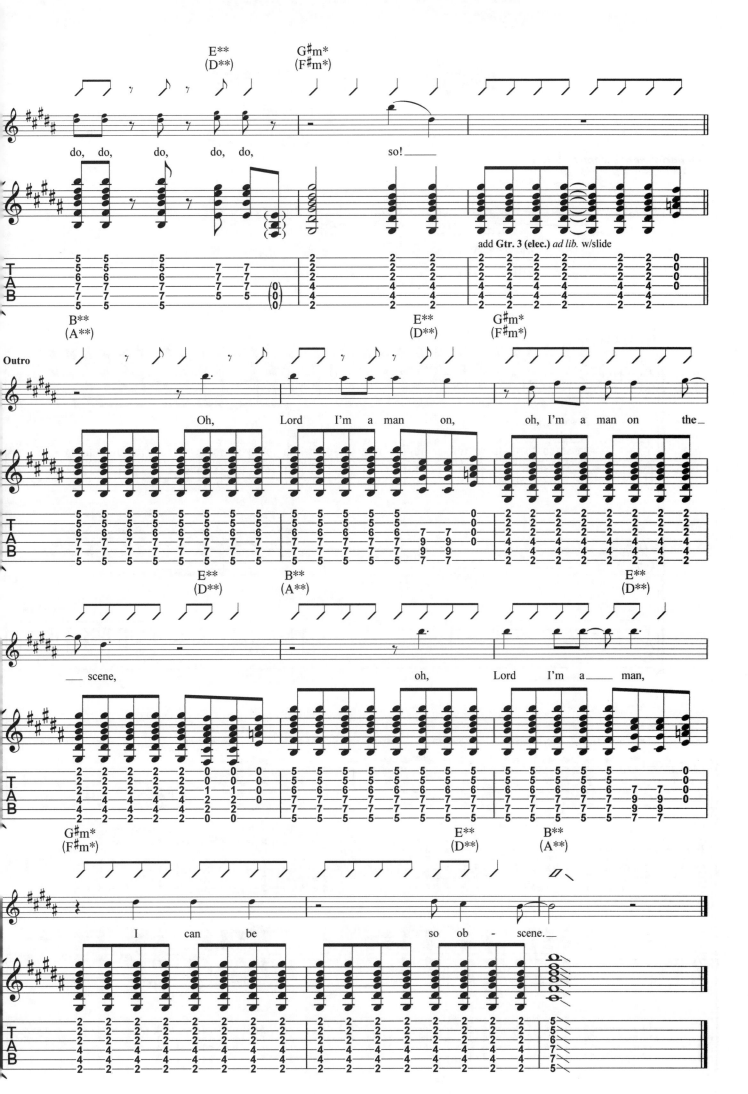

# eddie's gun

**Words & Music by Luke Pritchard**

**Full performance demo: CD track 2**
**Backing only: CD track 10**

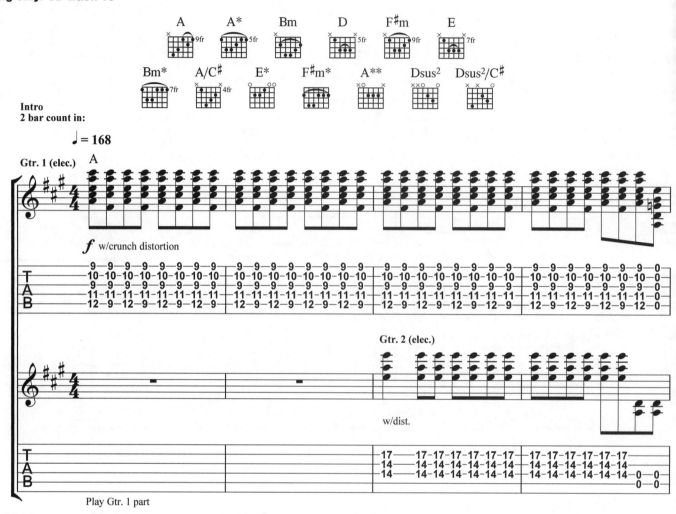

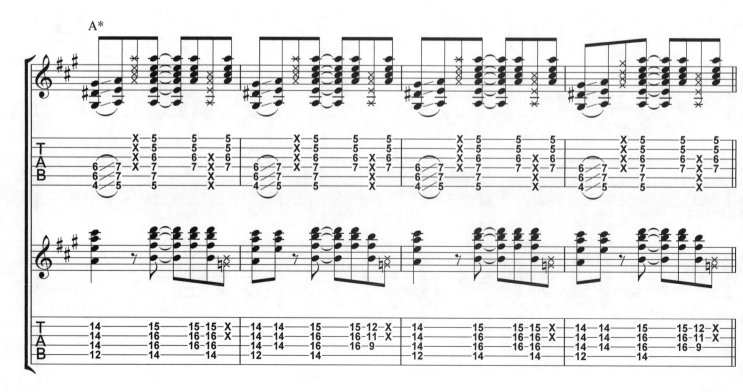

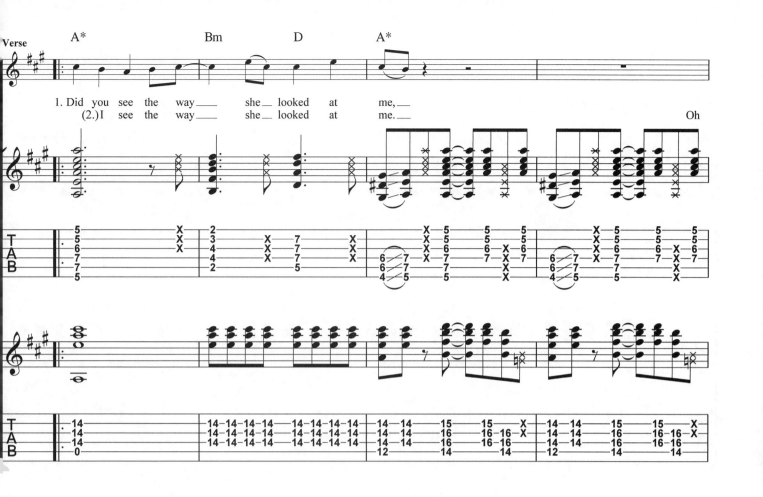

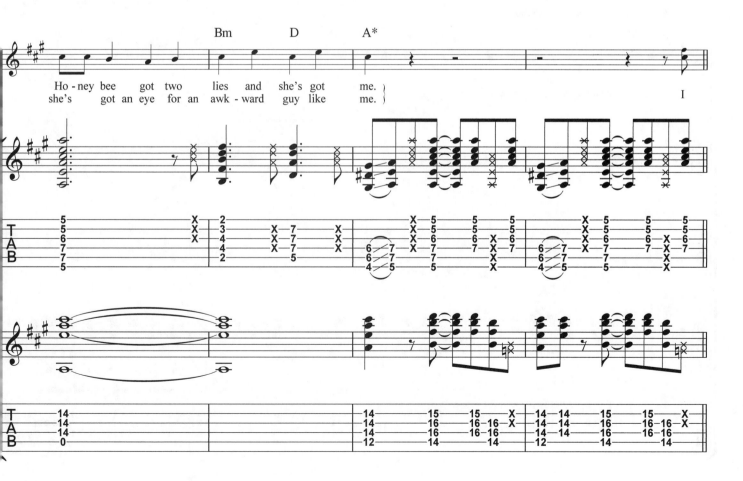

13

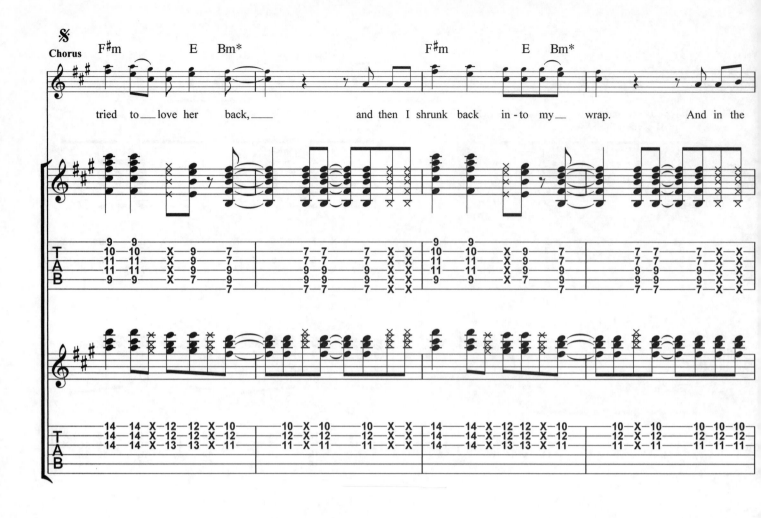

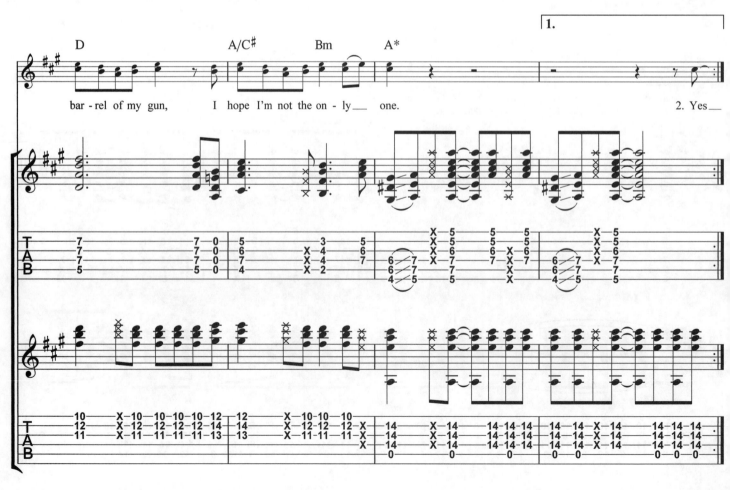

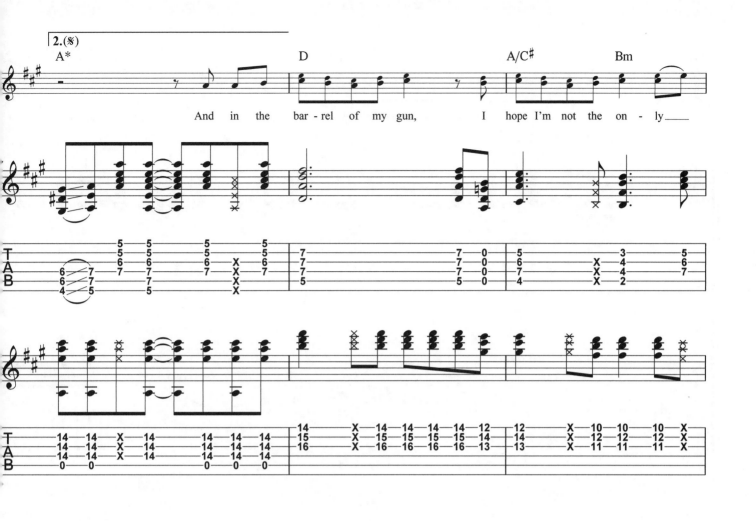

And in the bar-rel of my gun, I hope I'm not the on - ly\_\_\_

To Coda ⊕

one.

Yeah!

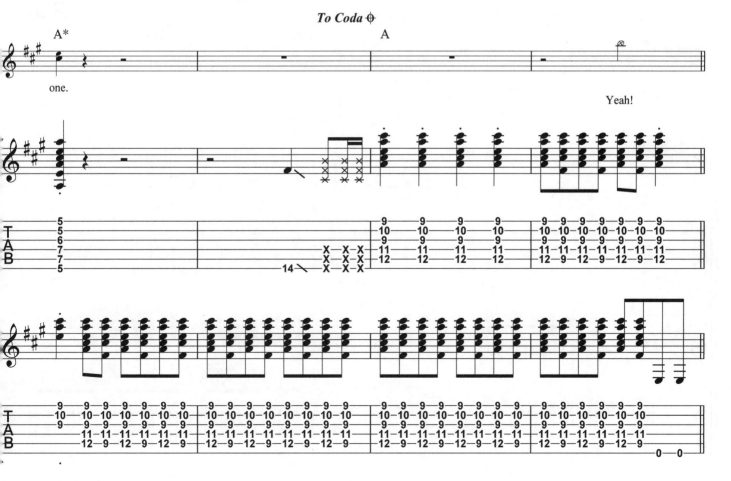

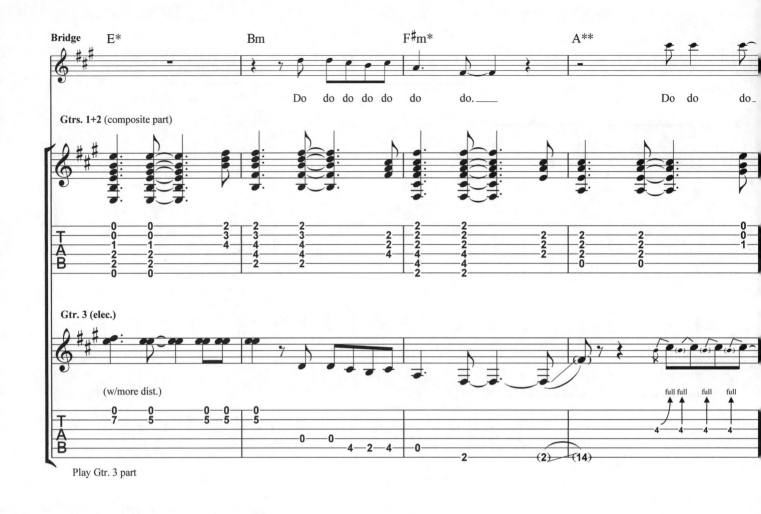

Play Gtr. 3 part

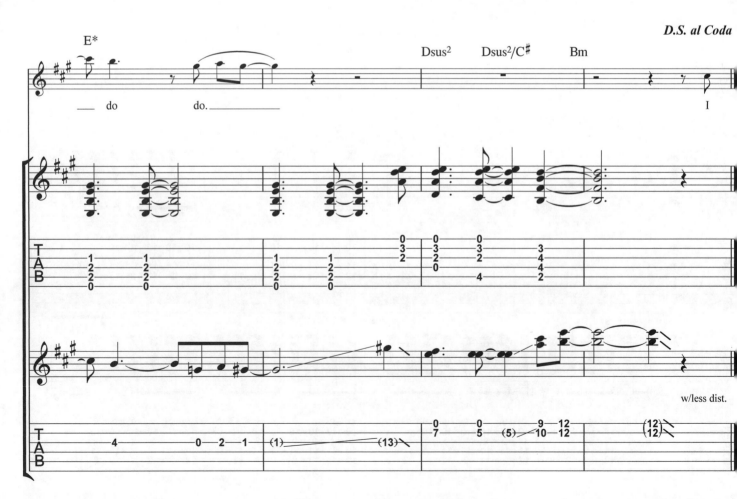

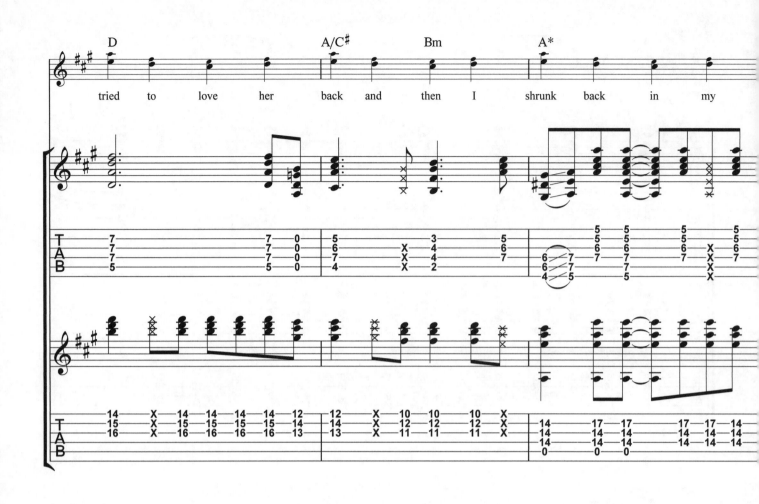

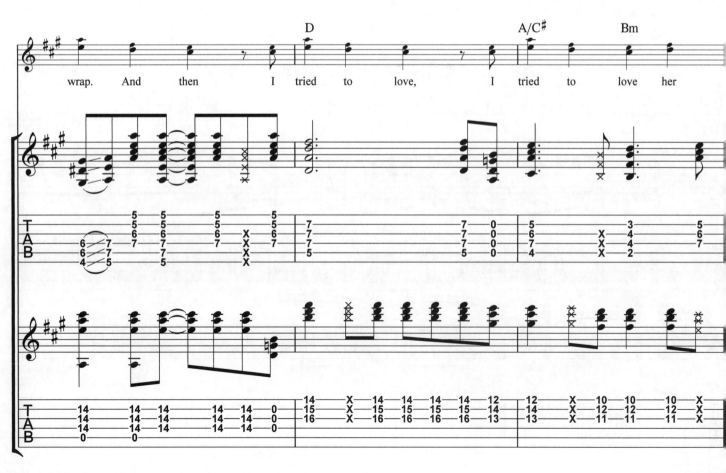

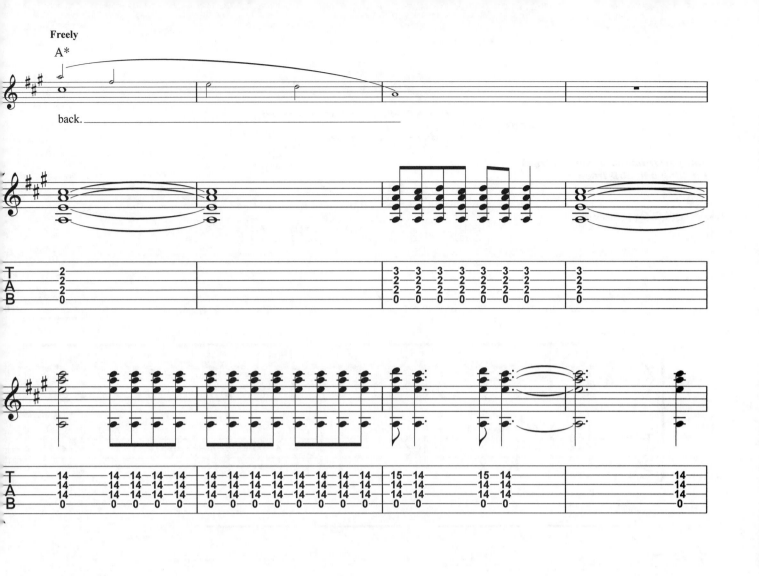

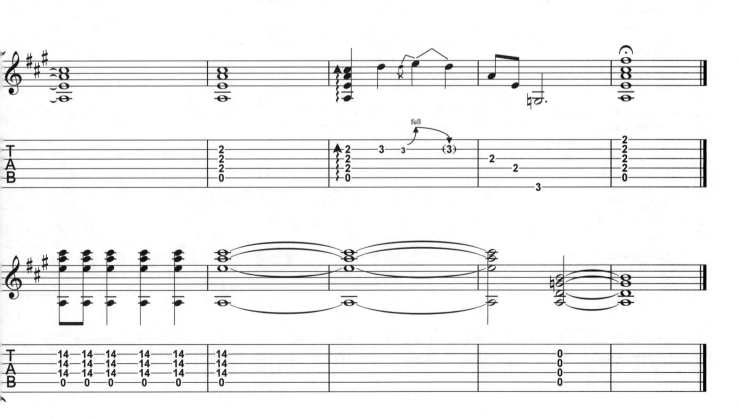

# ooh la

**Words & Music by Luke Pritchard**

**Full performance demo: CD track 3**
**Backing only: CD track 11**

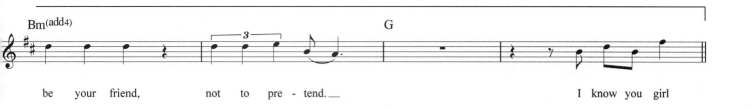

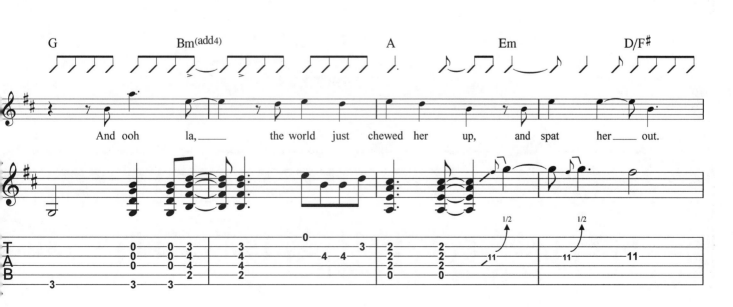

But ooh la,___ she was such a good girl___ to me.

hold…

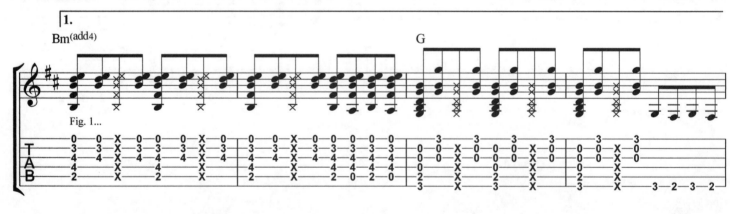

*To Coda* ⊕

And ooh la,___ the world just chewed her up, and spat her___ out.

**1.**

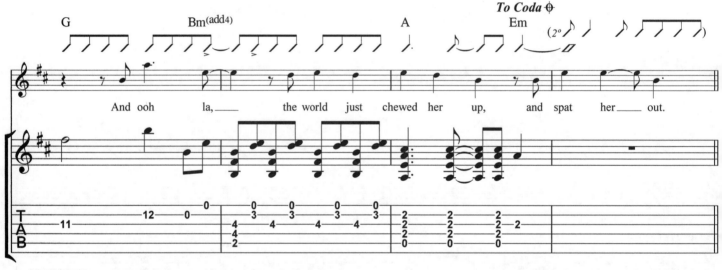

Fig. 1…

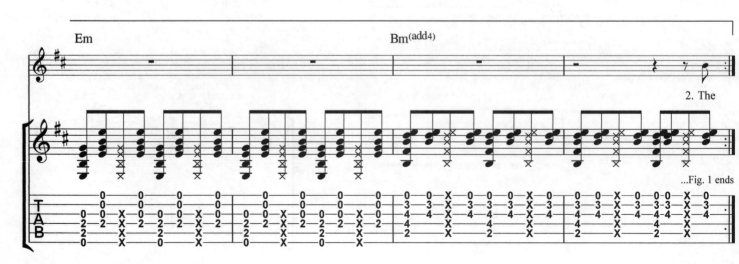

2. The

…Fig. 1 ends

22

**2.**

Bm<sup>(add4)</sup>                                    G

Gtr. 1 w/Fig. 1 *(x2)*

Pret - ty,    pret - ty,    pret - ty,    pret - ty,

Em                                               Bm<sup>(add4)</sup>

pret -ty,  pret -ty,  pret -ty,  pret -ty,    pret -ty,  pret -ty,  pret -ty,  pret -ty,    pet - ti - coat.

G

Pret -ty,  pret -ty,  pret -ty,  pret -ty,    pret -ty,  pret -ty,  pret -ty,  pret -ty,    pret -ty,  pret -ty,  pret -ty,  pret -ty,

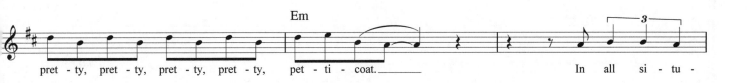

Em

pret -ty,  pret -ty,  pret -ty,  pret -ty,    pet - ti - coat.                    In   all   si - tu -

***D.S. al Coda***                    **Coda**

Gtrs. 1+2                                      Gtrs. 1+2
A                                              Em

- a -         tions.                                      spat  her___ out.

Gtr. 3 (elec.)                                 Gtr. 3

*mf*  let ring...
      w/crunch dist.

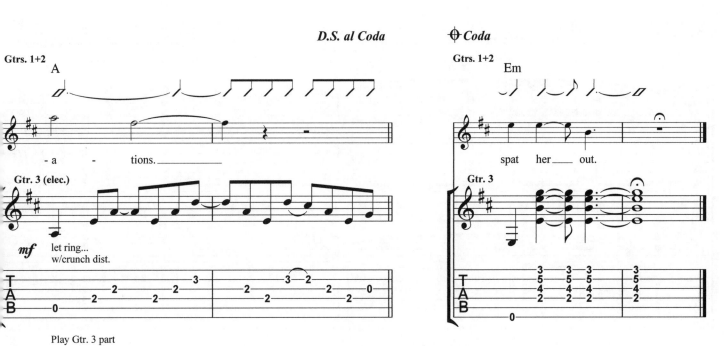

Play Gtr. 3 part

**23**

# naïve

**Words & Music by Luke Pritchard, Hugh Harris, Max Rafferty & Paul Garred**

**Full performance demo: CD track 4**
**Backing only: CD track 12**

Oh     and your sweet     and     pret - ty_____ face?_
Oh, you're    so    na - ïve, yeah so._____

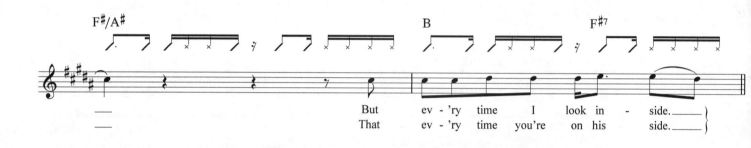

In such an    ug - ly way,_              for some - thing_ so beau - ti - ful._
It's such an    ug - ly thing,_           for some - one_ so beau - ti - ful._

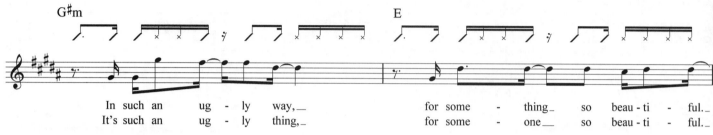

But    ev - 'ry time    I    look in - side._____ }
That    ev - 'ry time    you're    on his    side._____ }

*Gtr. 2 plays Eadd9
(chords as 1st chorus)

**Chorus**

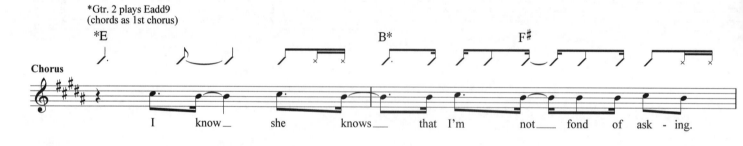

I    know_    she    knows_    that I'm    not_ fond    of ask - ing.

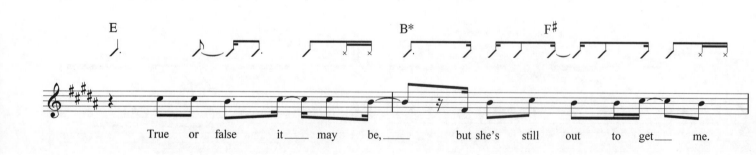

True    or    false    it_    may    be,_    but she's    still    out    to get_    me.

And    I    know_    she    knows_    that I'm    not_ fond    of ask - ing.

True or false it\_\_ may be,\_\_\_\_\_ but she's still out to get\_\_\_\_\_ me.\_\_\_\_

Ooh.\_\_\_\_

29

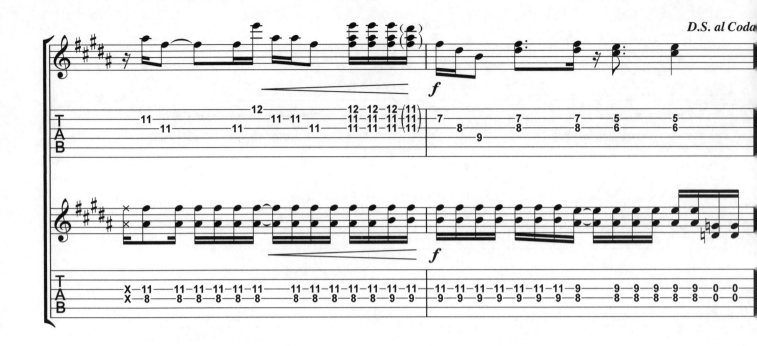

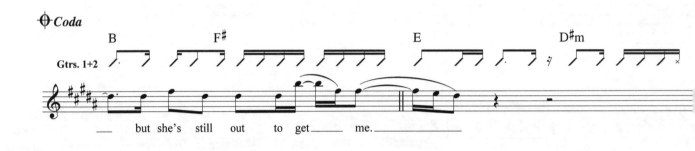

— but she's still out to get___ me.

Just don't let me down.                    Just don't let me down.___

Hold        on        to        your___ kite.        Just don't        let        me        down.___

Just don't        let        me        down.                    Just don't let me down.___

# shine on

**Words & Music by Luke Pritchard**

*Full performance demo: CD track 5*
*Backing only: CD track 13*

Play Gtr. 1 part

†Symbols in parentheses represent names with respect to capoed guitar.
Symbols above represent actual sounding chords (**Gtr. 1** tab 0 = Capo 6 fr.).

**Verse**

Gtr. 2  Gtr. 1
G♭  G♭            E♭m            C♭
(F)  (C)          (Am)           (F)

2° Gtr. 2

1. Safe-ty___ pins hold-ing up the things that make you mine.___
2. Your ma-ga-zines rip peo-ple at the seams, but you you still read.

*mf*  2° ad lib. sim.

A♭m            G♭            E♭m
(Dm)           (C)           (Am)

A-bout your___ hair you need-n't care, you look
I must ad-mit I don't be-lieve in it, but I

C♭            A♭m            A♭m
(F)           (Dm)           (Gm)†

Gtr. 2 (acous.)
Capo 1st fret

beau-ti-ful all of the___ time.
see how you get sucked___ in.

†Symbols in parentheses represent chord names for
Gtr. 2 rhythm slashes only.

**Chorus**

A♭            D♭            G♭            D♭
(G)           (C)           (F)           (C)

Shine, shine, shine on,___ yes,___

*f*

34

shine, shine on,___

The safe-ty___ pins hold-ing up the things that make you mine.___

A-bout your_ hair you need-n't care, you look beau-ti-ful all of the___ time.

# she moves in her own way

**Words & Music by Luke Pritchard & Hugh Harris**

**Full performance demo: CD track 6**
**Backing only: CD track 14**

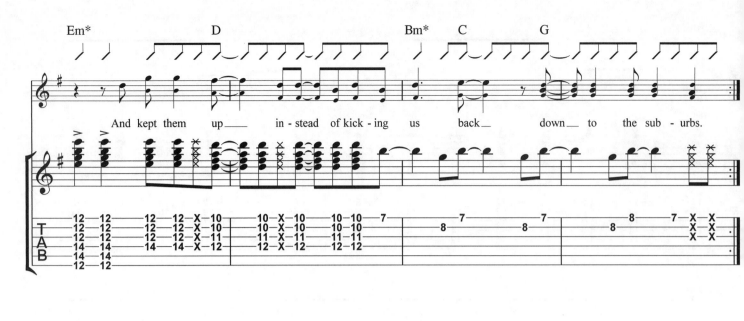

And kept them up___ in-stead of kick-ing us back___ down___ to the sub-urbs.

**Solo**

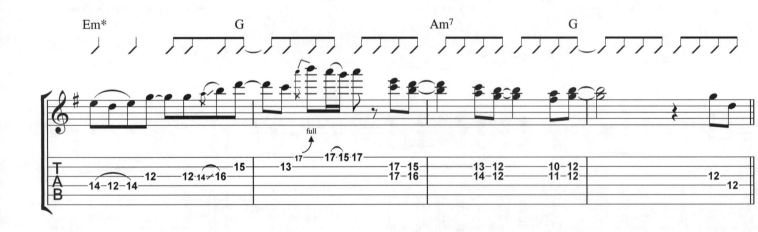

(w/more dist.)

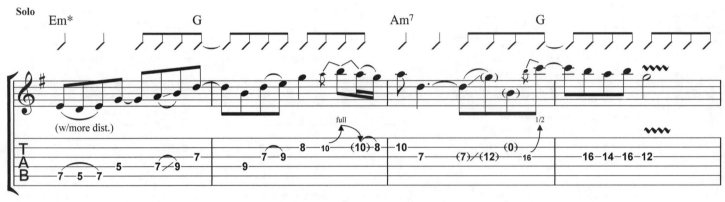

**Chorus**

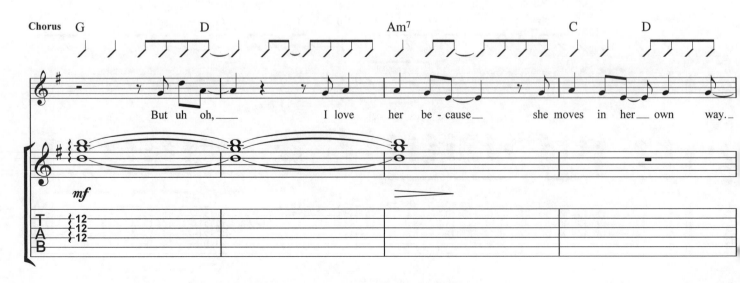

But uh oh,___ I love her be-cause___ she moves in her___ own way.___

# sway

**Words & Music by Luke Pritchard**

**Full performance demo: CD track 7**
**Backing only: CD track 15**

†Symbols in parentheses represent names with respect to capoed guitar.
Symbols above represent actual sounding chords.

Play Gtr. 2 part

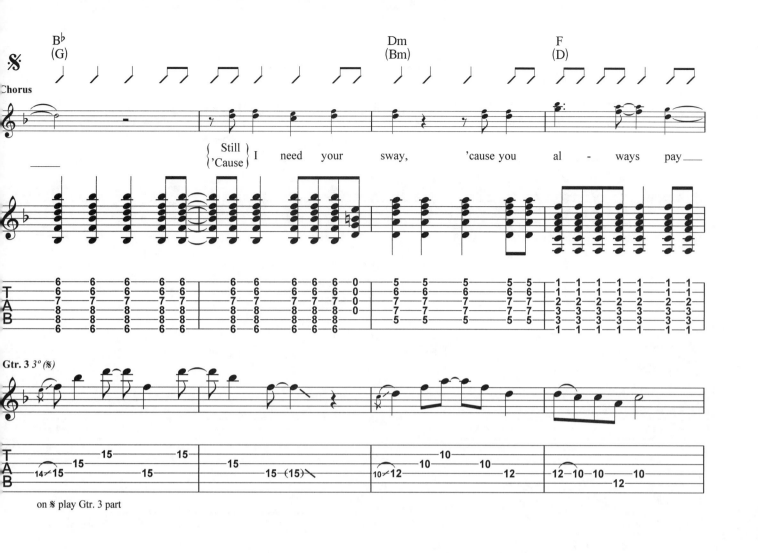

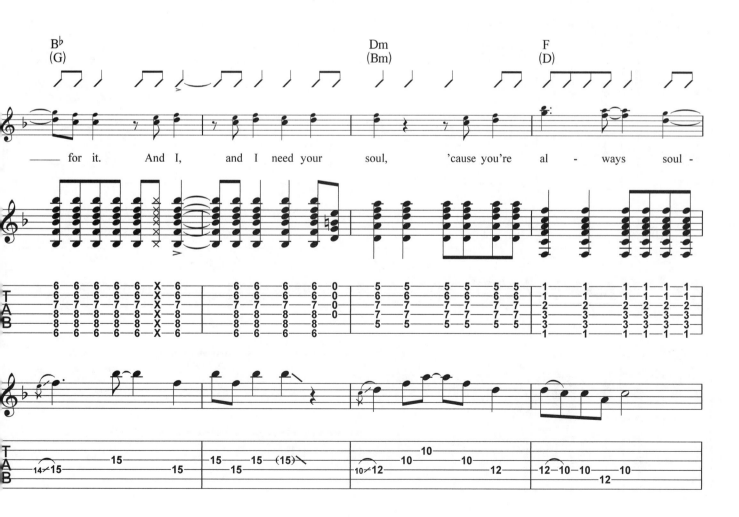

al - ways__ in the right__ pla - ces.

*Capo 3rd fret (Tab 0 = 3fr)

# you don't love me

**Words & Music by Luke Pritchard, Hugh Harris, Max Rafferty & Paul Garred**

**Full performance demo: CD track 8**
**Backing only: CD track 16**

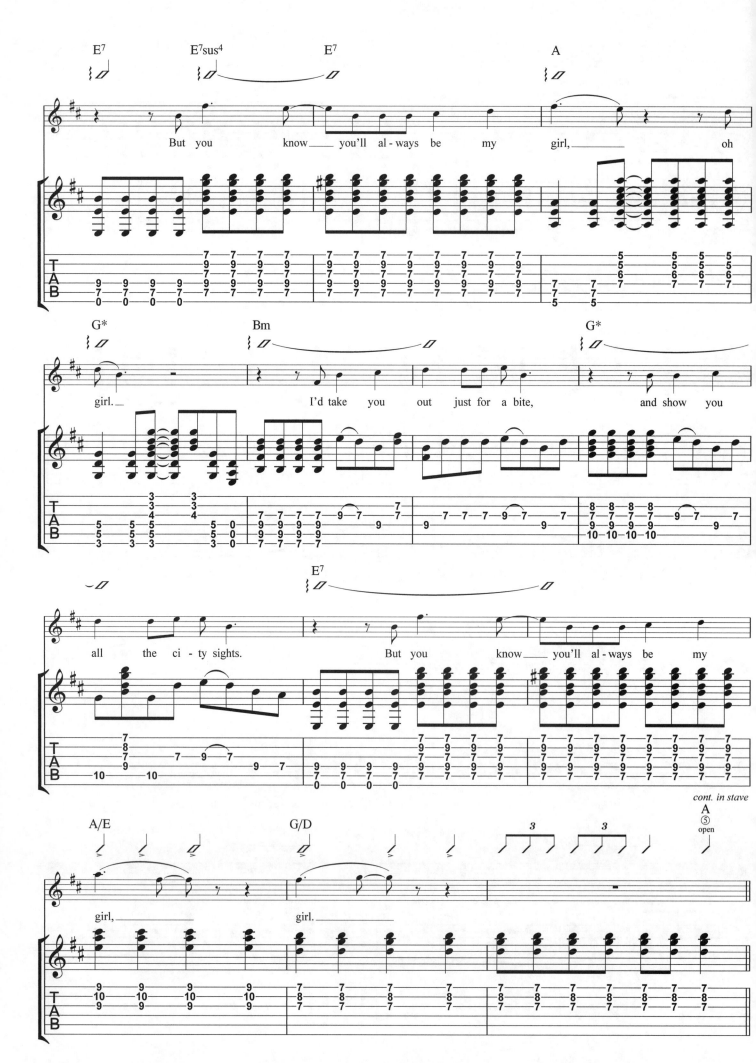

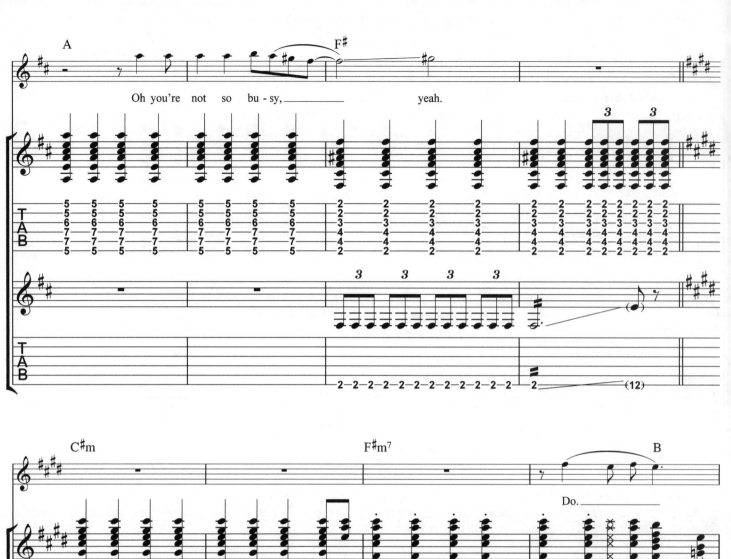

Oh you're not so bu-sy,_____ yeah.

Do._____

Fig. 3...

...Fig. 3 ends

Gtr. 3

w/fuzz dist.

Play Gtr. 3 part

Do, do, do.

Gtr. 1 w/Fig.3

# CD track listing

**Full instrumental performances (with guitar)...**

1 **always where i need to be**
(Pritchard)
Sony/ATV Harmony UK.

2 **eddie's gun**
(Pritchard)
Sony/ATV Harmony UK.

3 **ooh la**
(Pritchard)
Sony/ATV Harmony UK.

4 **naïve**
(Pritchard/Harris/Rafferty/Garred)
Sony/ATV Harmony UK.

5 **shine on**
(Pritchard)
Sony/ATV Harmony UK.

6 **she moves in her own way**
(Pritchard/Harris)
Sony/ATV Harmony UK.

7 **sway**
(Pritchard)
Sony/ATV Harmony UK.

8 **you don't love me**
(Pritchard/Harris/Rafferty/Garred)
Sony/ATV Harmony UK.

**Backing tracks only (without guitar)...**

9 **always where i need to be**

10 **eddie's gun**

11 **ooh la**

12 **naïve**

13 **shine on**

14 **she moves in her own way**

15 **sway**

16 **you don't love me**

---

To remove your CD from the plastic sleeve, lift the small lip on the side to break the perforated flap. Replace the disc after use for convenient storage.